# MOONSTRUCK!

## Poems About Our Moon

**Acknowledgements**
Brian Moses, 'To the Moon' is from *Lost Magic: The Very Best of Brian Moses* (Macmillan, 2016)

'Moon Poem of the Nandi Children' is from is from *The Nandi: Their Language and Folklore* by A.C. Hollis (Oxford University Press, 1909)

First published in paperback in Great Britain in 2019 by
Otter-Barry Books
Little Orchard, Burley Gate, Hereford, HR1 3QS

www.otterbarrybooks.com

A catalogue record for this book is available
from the British Library.

Designed by Arianna Osti

ISBN 978-1-91095-965-7

Illustrated with ink drawings and linoprints

Printed in the United Kingdom

1 3 5 7 9 8 6 4 2

# MOONSTRUCK!

## Poems About Our Moon

Edited by
**Roger Stevens**

Illustrated by
**Ed Boxall**

Otter-Barry BOOKS

# Contents

# When I Was Three

Mother made us
come inside
from the backyard.
How odd.
She sat us down,
my sister and me,
in front of our glowing
and hissing TV
and pointed at the screen.
She told us
those grainy shadows
swirling
in black and white and grey,
were the feet of a man
far, far away.
That right now
he was standing

on the moon.

"Imagine," she said.

I wanted to return
to the world of my backyard –
to my sandbox
and my swing set.
"Not yet," she said.
"Watch."
And I did.
"Remember," she said.
And I do.

*Eric Ode*

# The Eagle Has Landed

Did I feel nervous?
Well, I'd hoped we'd have more time
for preparations.
Our chances?
Fifty-fifty we would land.
And only one in ten we'd make it home again.
It's further than you think, the Moon,
two hundred thousand miles away.
So, was I nervous?
Yes, I'd say.

We climbed atop the giant Saturn V,
began the checks,
I smiled at Michael and at Buzz,
they smiled at me.

Five and four and three and two and one... lift off.
The engine's noise a thousand devils, singing
tunelessly
as through the smoke and steam and fire we rose.
The last stage of the rocket tumbled to the sun.

Whilst Michael orbited the Moon
we took the lunar module down
on to that tranquil sea.
Buzz thought the Moon looked desolate,
lifeless and empty.

White and black and every shade of grey between.
But I thought, No –
the Moon is beautiful
and like no other place I've ever seen.

And should you ever visit it
these words you'll find:
*Here men from the planet Earth*
*First set foot upon the Moon.*
*We came in peace, for all mankind.*

*Roger Stevens*

# The Lonely Side
# of the Moon

Billions
(plus two)
on the other
side. But over
here, it's just                    me
and radio
silence.

*Laura Mucha*

Many people still know the names of the two first men on the Moon, but few remember the third astronaut on the Apollo 11 mission. When Armstrong and Aldrin launched towards the Moon, it was Michael Collins' job to meet them afterwards. As he swept behind the Moon in his spacecraft, *Columbia*, he was separated for 48 minutes from the rest of humanity by 250,000 miles of space and the Moon, which blocked all radio transmissions to and from mission control.

# A Note from an Astronaut

A hammer and a feather
are two very different things.
One is made for pounding nails,
the other gives you wings.

One is quite a heavy tool,
the other oh-so-light.
So what will likely happen
if we drop them from a height?

The pair of them will fall, of course
(they're hardly going to climb!)
and both will land together
at *precisely* the same time.

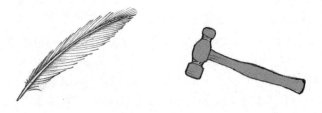

'What?' you say. 'Preposterous!
That clearly can't be true.'
It's true alright, it worked for me,
though maybe won't for you.

'And why is that?' You glower,
screw your face up like a prune.
Because, my friend, I did it
on the surface of the moon.

*Yours,*
*David Scott*
*Apollo 15 Commander*

*Shauna Darling Robertson*

Note: In 1971, Apollo 15 Commander David Scott stood on
the Moon and dropped a hammer and a feather from the
same height at the same time. They both landed at the
same time because there's no air on the Moon to create
resistance.

# What Am I?

My first is in asteroid
Not in rock
My second in Space
Not in dock

Third is in orbit
Not in stars
Fourth is in landing
Not in Mars

Fifth is in light-year
Not in away
Next is in Moon
Not Milky Way

My last is a number
Which rhymes with heaven
Just one clue
It is not number seven.

*Debra Bertulis*

ANSWER:

(Apollo 11)

# To the Moon

It has been just the luck of a privileged few
to walk on the moon and look back at the view,
to stare at the planet they left behind
and to wonder if anything else they could find
would ever be quite so breathtaking as this,
no fast car ride, no daughter's kiss,
could ever come close to this mountain top,
this pinnacle, this unearthly drop.

And then after the tears and the interviews
and the general hullabaloo,
and the hundreds of times you walk through a door
to talk on TV and describe what you saw,
the realisation still hits far too soon,
what do you do now you've been to the Moon?

*Brian Moses*

# The Moon is a Starfish

The moon is a starfish
Swimming in the sky
It reaches bright tentacles
Across the Earth
To feed on pockets of darkness

*Valerie Bloom*

# Moon Poem of the Nandi Children

When the moon is new
The children, if they are Nandi,
When the moon is new,
They spit at it and they say
Welcome moon!
If you eat anything, may it choke you
If I eat anything may it do me good.
If the old men see the moon,
They say to it
Pst! Guard the children and the cattle
Come, moon in your goodness,
Guard the children and the cattle,
Then guard me until you die.

Here is the original in Nandi:

Arawet ne-ko-lel
Ingo-'ro lakõk-ap-Nandi
Arawet ne-ko-lel,
Ko-ñgut-yi ko-'le-chi
Pelepele arawa!
Ingi-am kii, ko-'ket-in
Ingã-am-ki, ko-'is-a.
Ingo-'ro poiisiek arawet,
ko-'le-chi
'Ptu, tuk-u-a lakok ak tuka
Nyo arawá-ni ne-mie,
Tuk-u-a lakuk ak tuka,
Tuk-u-a koi tun ingi-me.

*Traditional: Kenya*

21

# Moon

In my name are the eyes of the owl,
the wheels of my turning,
the call of the cow who leapt.
Look on me, in my name
is the ooh
of midnight waking.

*Mandy Coe*

# Daytime Moon

Today we were driving home
from seeing our grandpa
and grandma on the other
side of town and it was still
bright daylight, even though
it was late, almost bedtime
and I looked out of the car
window and suddenly saw
a small, pale eye of silver
stone blinking down at me
through the white clouds
and where the jet planes
had scratched deep smoky
plumes through the blue.
I turned to tell my mum
but she was falling asleep,
my dad was busy driving
and telling my little sister
to stop going on about
princesses and unicorns,
not to mention pink ponies
and all that claptrap, his
words not mine, so finally
it was just me and the Moon
looking at each other in
broad daylight. I poked Mum
quite hard in the side to wake

her up but by the time she'd
finished saying WHAT?
and OW the sly, slippery,
moon-shiny eye-ball
had winked and was gone.

*David Harmer*

# The Oak and the Moon

Late one April afternoon I saw the Moon
Caught in the outmost reach of an oak
Held fast in her cradle of wood
Biding her time
For the wind to shake her free.

*Catherine Benson*

# Firework Night, Full Moon

Quiet as toads
On a low hill
A tight crowd
Ogles flashes
Of high fire

While a girl
In a green coat
Sees the moon
Beribboned
With blue smoke

*Steven Withrow*

# Moon-Mad

Look at the moon!
A crescent sky-ship sailing
out of a cloudy cocoon

Look at the moon!
A cauldron of amber
spelling, rain-come-soon

Look at the moon!
A Mexican gold plate
over Montezuma's tomb

Look at the moon!
A full-blown O
(I was trying to avoid the word balloon)

Just open the window of your room
and look at the wolf-raising
sea-swelling shape-shifting
myth-making
Earth-watching moon
holding us
in the bloom of a moon-lock

*Grace Nichols*

# The Delicious Side
# of the Moon

I search the night sky for the Moon
And instead, I find a cake
I stare at it, for it must be special
As it glows brightly in a strange vanilla white
Another night, I glance up
And a white coconut looks back at me
Days wear on and I grow curious again
What food item will the sky hold?
My eyes scan the sky
And I find a complete half of a white pancake
The sight makes me drool
There is a rather pointy banana on another night
And a deformed burger on another
I look up on a random night
Hoping for a pointy sausage
And instead I find darkness
And I can picture the sky scolding me
"You should not eat so much."

*Harshita Das (aged 12)*

# Eight Ways to Get to the Moon

Be fired from a super-charged cannon
Bend back the largest tree in the world, sit on
   a branch
and yell "Release!" to your friend
Stack up a million elephants and climb to the moon
Ask a spaceman to take you to the ISS, and use
   an escape pod
to land you on the moon
Travel in a time machine back to the age of the
   flying reptiles
and ride a quetzalcoatlus to the moon
Fly there on a plasma dragon
Invite the Man in the Moon to tea, and afterwards
   get a lift back to his home
Build a rainmaker on a sunny day, switch it on
   to make a rainbow
and run up the rainbow to the moon
And finally, decadilate the flamoralator of the
kabooshidoo, climb in
insert the key into the plofflumator and it will
send you there in an instant

*Sam Decie (aged 9)*

# Questions to Ask the Moon

Does your Earth side rejoice
when from your lunar night
the white sun rises suddenly
to a bright and cloudless
light?

Does your Earth side gaze
at the Earth's wax and wane
full Earth to crescent Earth
       which disappears and comes again?

    Does your Earth side sleep
     when your two-week day is done
      and dark falls with no colours
       to switch off your spotlight sun?

    Does your dark side weep
     for a soft earthlight at night
    with its patterns ever changing
as it turns through blue and white?

*Liz Brownlee*

# When Billy Found a Fossil in a Moonrock

Look, Billy said
it's the jawbone
of an alien dinosaur.
*Where?*
Right there,
you can see it quite clearly.
In the moonrock.
An alien dinosaur
that roamed the moon
a million years ago.
*Are you sure it's a moonrock?*
Billy smiled and said,
Yes, I found it by the light
of a full moon.

*Roger Stevens*

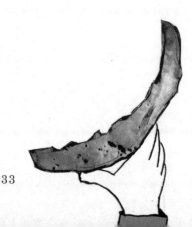

# Dear Mr Astronaut

I'd really like some moon dust,
Do you have any to spare?
I've seen your photo on the Web,
So I know that you've been there.

I've got some handmade beads from Africa,
A mask from Kathmandu,
A hair from a Tibetan yak,
And a stick from Timbuktu.
I've a feather from an ostrich,
Some sand from Byron Bay,
An ammonite, a raptor tooth,
And an owl from Mandalay.
I've a geode from South Africa,
A drumstick from The Who.
A medal from my grandad that he got in
    World War 2.
A bobble-headed Einstein,
And a conch shell from Belize,
A coin from 1893,
And a bunch of antique keys.

But...
if I only had some moon dust.
I'd really love some moon dust.
(I had to take this chance.)
Please, please...
could you spare some moon dust?
And THANK YOU! (In advance.)


Yours Very Hopefully
Charlotte Age 10 ½

*Doda Smith*

# The First Woman
# on the Moon

Little known fact:
the first woman on the moon
was Mabel Greensmith.

She went up there in a dream
in 1959
and when she woke up
she knew her dream was true.

Mabel was my mum's best friend
so, of course, she told my mum
all about going to the moon
and my mum told me.
And then we all forgot about it.

However, ten years later, in 1969,
when Neil Armstrong walked on the moon
('one giant leap for mankind')
it was regarded as a big deal.

But he went up in a proper rocket
and had to wear a spacesuit
whereas Mabel did her moon walking
wearing only a pair of slippers
and a flannelette nightie,
and with her hair in rollers.

If Mabel had been in the papers
and on TV
it would have been great
but she wasn't one for a lot of fuss
and continued to live quietly
as one of us.

Though it's a shame she didn't leave a slipper
or one of her rollers up there
for Neil Armstrong to discover.
That really would have put the earth cat
among the moon pigeons.

*Bernard Young*

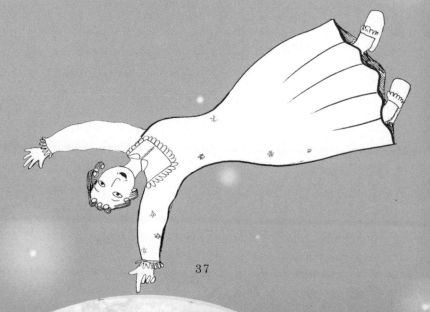

37

# The Moon Speaks!

*I, the moon,*
*would like it known – I*
*never follow people home. I*
*simply do not have the time. And*
*neither do I ever shine. For what you*
*often see at night is me reflecting solar*
*light. And I'm not cheese! No, none of*
*these: no mozzarellas, cheddars, bries, all*
*you'll find here – if you please – are my*
*dusty, empty seas. And cows do not*
*jump over me. Now that is simply*
*lunacy! You used to come and*
*visit me. Oh do return,*
*I'm lonely, see.*

*James Carter*

# Winter Night on a Rocky Coast

Like galloping horses across the headlands,
    waters rage and roar.

Reign in your tides, Moon! Tame those wild
   mustangs
      beating up the shore.

*Cynthia Grady*

# You

You intergalactic car crash,
You shrapnel of a bygone age,
You mother,
You watcher,
You God.

You who watched the Earth burn,
You who saw it reborn,
Who saw life spread.
You who called to dreamers,
To scientists,
To lovers,
To priests,
To kings.
You who called to us,

Every one of us,
From before time existed.

You who is constant,
Yet constantly changing.

You who calls to the seas
To set their rhythm,

Who tells these watery lungs
To breathe.

You who infiltrated dreams,
In every age of man,
Who asked artists
To do more,
To be more,
To be immortal,
Like you.


*Jay Hulme*

# To the Moon

Art thou pale for weariness
Of climbing heaven and gazing on the earth,
Wandering companionless
Among the stars that have a different birth,
And ever changing, like a joyless eye
That finds no object worth its constancy?

*Percy Bysshe Shelley (1792–1822)*

# The Cruel Truth

Truth is, Moon
that it's only the close circle you move in
that makes you so attractive.

You're 'B' list,
a lesser celebrity,
the Sun's the star

and it's only because you bask
in the Sun's reflected  glory
that we ever focus on you.

The cruel truth is, Moon
that compared with a star
you don't have the pulling power.

*Philip Waddell*

# Three Short Poems

### 1

Inside the dark box
a huge pearl shines like silver.
Oh, the magic glow!

### 2

From whose great necklace,
or from what giant coffer,
have you been stolen?
How will we keep your brightness
safe within the night's dark purse?

### 3

Tear drop,
you are so vast.
Did you spill from God's eye,
as seeing the world's sadness made
him cry?

*Tony Mitton*

Three poems written in the style of a haiku, a tanka
and a cinquain

# Poor Old Phoebe!

Some thought her a god
and worshipped her on their knees.
Others, not so kind,
said she was made of cheese
until, in 1969,
without so much as a pretty please,
they walked all over her, even cut
pieces from her lunar gut.
Yet still she shines
in poets' lines,
none of her romance gone,
despite being trodden upon.

*Celia Warren*

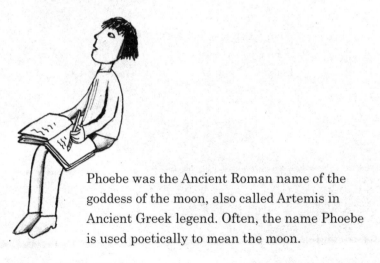

Phoebe was the Ancient Roman name of the
goddess of the moon, also called Artemis in
Ancient Greek legend. Often, the name Phoebe
is used poetically to mean the moon.

# Moon Marks

You bear the scars of asteroids
cratering your crust,
a dozen spaceman footsteps
imprinted in your dust.

Since you have no wind or rain
those footprints will remain,
perhaps until an asteroid
smashes into you again.

*B.J. Lee*

# Moon Magic

the moon gilds the sea
with lilypads of light

if they were stepping stones
I would walk that path
across the dark green water

step on golden gleams and stride
over fish and seals beyond all tides

then up I'd step from sea to sky
walking the moon path
learning to fly

*Jan Dean*

# Moonlight

Moonlight
    Moonlight
is
    is
sunlight
    sunlight
bouncing
    bouncing
off the moon.
    off the moon.
The sun's
    The sun's
why
    why
the moon casts
    the moon casts
a silvery
    a silvery
glow.
    glow.
Turn
    Turn
your back on it,
    your back on it,

look
    look
down –
    down –
moon shadow.
    moon shadow.

Trevor Parsons
    Trevor Parsons

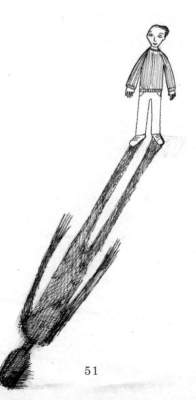

# Evidence of Alien Life

In deep time
like a schooner
the space creature
one hundred miles long
its thick silicon skin
peppered with space rock
sails on the solar winds
leaves its footprints
craters in the crust
of the moon

*Roger Stevens*

# Moonlight, Summer Moonlight

'Tis moonlight, summer moonlight,
All soft and still and fair;
The solemn hour of midnight
Breathes sweet thoughts everywhere,

But most where trees are sending
Their breezy boughs on high,
Or stooping low are lending
A shelter from the sky.

And there in those wild bowers
A lovely form is laid;
Green grass and dew-steeped flowers
Wave gently round her head.

*Emily Brontë (1818–1848)*

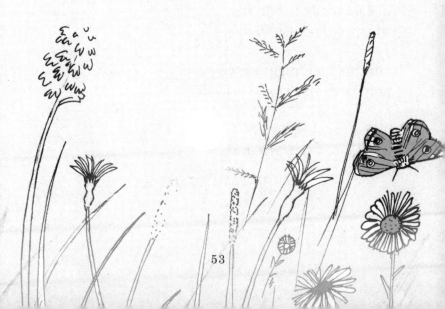

# No Such Thing

*There's no such thing*
*as moonlight,* they say.
But –

I've bathed in it, played in it,
stayed up too late in it,

walked with it, stalked it
and talked girl-to-orb with it,

danced till I'm numb in it,
stuck out my tongue at it,

jumped over cows with it,
made secret vows to it,

tickled white fish in it,
whispered a wish to it,

munched midnight snacks in it,
practised wise-cracks with it,

drifted to sleep in it,
knelt down to weep in it,

hugged the cool breeze,
splashed in warm seas
leapt high as fleas
and scuffed both my knees in it.

No such thing
as moonlight?
*Please!*

*Shauna Darling Robertson*

Note: Technically there's no such thing as moonlight. It's
really a reflection of the sun's light on the moon's surface
(or so they say!).

# Three Short Moon Poems

1
moontide waters lap
the moon-shadowed beach
glint of blue moonglass

2
Moon in my tumbler
shimmering in the water
I drink the moon

3
eye in the night sky
tree shadows in the moonlight
following the hare

*Roger Stevens*

# Good Moon, Bad Moon

"Good Moon," said Turtle, "when you're full
The ocean answers to your pull,
The tide creeps higher and I reach
The best egg-laying bits of beach."

"Bad Moon," said Moth, "I like to fly
When darkness covers earth and sky,
But when you flood the dark with light
I don't know whether to take flight."

"Good Moon," said Coral, "when you shine
We corals see it as a sign
It's nearly time for us to spawn,
So beautiful new reefs are born."

"Bad Moon," said Lion, "my best prey
Avoids your light and hides away,
So when you're brightest I must run
And hunt under the scorching sun."

"Good Moon," said Eagle Owl, "I know
My feathery white throat will show
Most clearly in your silver gleam,
So when you're full I pose and preen."

"Bad Moon," said Bat, "you're much too bright.
I hunt my prey in darkest night,
But when you're shining overhead
I worry *I'll* be prey instead."

Said Moon, "I am not bad or good.
You creatures haven't understood.
I cannot choose how bright I shine,
My brightness changes over time.

Be patient, Lion, Moth and Bat.
Just wait a while.  I promise that
My light will soon begin to wane,
And night-time will be dark again."

*Julia Rawlinson*

# Moonstruck

Moonstruck
A brilliant idea that arrives after midnight
Moonsick
When you live in the city and you long to catch
moonbeams
Moonstick
A branch cut for walking across moonlit fields
Moonsack
A bag made of memories for storing your dreams

*Roger Stevens*

# The Moon

The moon has a face like the clock in the hall;
She shines on thieves on the garden wall,
On streets and fields and harbour quays,
And birdies asleep in the forks of the trees.

The squalling cat and the squeaking mouse,
The howling dog by the door of the house,
The bat that lies in bed at noon,
All love to be out by the light of the moon.

But all of the things that belong to the day
Cuddle to sleep to be out of her way;
And flowers and children close their eyes
Till up in the morning the sun shall arise.

*Robert Louis Stevenson (1850–1894)*

# Hymn to the Moon

Thou silver deity of secret night,
Direct my footsteps through the woodland shade;
Thou conscious witness of unknown delight,
The Lover's guardian, and the Muse's aid!
By thy pale beams I solitary rove,
To thee my tender grief confide;
Serenely sweet you gild the silent grove,
My friend, my goddess, and my guide.
E'en thee, fair queen, from thy amazing height,
The charms of young Endymion drew;
Veil'd with the mantle of concealing night;
With all thy greatness and thy coldness too.

*Lady Mary Wortley Montagu (1689–1762)*

# In the Arms of the Moon

Dawn sits in the arms of the moon
Weaving songs of spider silk
Collects the stars on a silver spoon
And cleans the sky with buttermilk
Morning paints the clouds in the sky
And fashions a gown of mist
Waking Day with a lullaby
Made bright by an angel's kiss
Evening sits in the arms of the moon
Washing the colours from the world
Night wraps his tears in oyster shells
And fills the sea with pearls

*Sue Hardy-Dawson*

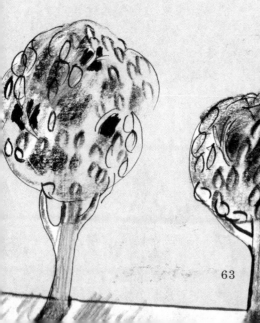

# Moontime

Old Moon warns us to be wise.
Snow Moon stirs the heavy skies.
And a Sap Moon slowly rises.

Egg Moon nestles in our palm.
Milk Moon brings the blossom's balm.
And a Rose Moon shows its charm.

Hay Moon lines the cattle shed.
Grain Moon offers broth and bread.
And a Harvest Moon turns red.

Blood Moon tugs the flesh from bone.
Frost Moon hardens soil to stone.
Then a Cold Moon takes us home.

*Rachel Rooney*

# Autumn

I walked abroad,
And saw the ruddy moon lean over a hedge
Like a red-faced farmer.
I did not stop to speak, but nodded,
And round about were the wistful stars
With white faces like town children.

*T. E. Hulme (1883–1917)*

# Moony Names

Wolf teaser
Myth crafter
Shape shifter

Night galleon
Star schooner
Tide lifter

Old timer
Slow climber
Beam maker

Earth's daughter
Sky voyager
Spook waker

Star shepherd
Night watchman
Earth looper

Night stalker
Earth gawker
Moth duper

*Philip Waddell and Roger Stevens*

# Sorry

I am
the black cat of night
and I am sorry
that I played
so roughly
with the silver ball
and now all
that is left
is a slight slender shard
of light
tomorrow I promise
I will begin
to put it together again

*Trevor Millum*

# Moon Moth

Mad moth,
moon moth,
beating on the glass,
powdering the window pane,
chasing after false moons,
bright in our house,
wingbeat a pattering of rain.

Mad moth,
moon moth,
panic in your wings,
fly far away down the street,
As we draw the curtains,
escape the circus rings;
dance to the true moonbeat.

*Celia Warren*

# Moon Canvas

If I painted the moon
I would need lots of yellow, mixed with white
to make it bright
And some rich, dark ultramarine for the night sky
and I would make the tree shadows black, ebony
   black
Then I would call creatures of the night
in muted colours
browns and olive greens
to dance upon my canvas
in the pinks and scarlets and shining oranges
of the hidden sun

*Roger Stevens*

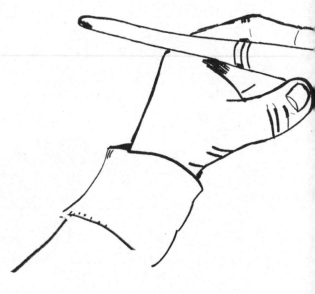

# Hearing from the Moon

At the day's end the moon sits milky and pale
Till darkness descends and she gleams
And crawls up the sky just as slow as a snail
Suspended on slender moonbeams.

As full moon or new moon, she rides her high trail
Between the real world and our dreams,
Her silence unbroken, unspoken; no tale
To unveil her thoughts, themes and schemes.

She's eyeless. If only our moon could use braille
She'd read us her story in reams;
Or maybe it's us and our senses that fail
To catch lunar language which streams

From her down to us like a storm or a gale
When rainfall relentlessly teems.
If so, then we miss it, this lost Holy Grail.
Oh, nothing is quite what it seems.

*Nick Toczek*

# The Moon and the Frost

Welcome, first hint of winter. Welcome ghost night
with your three-quarter moon outshining stars.
A criminal frost steals in to harden fallen leaves
and draw spiralling graffiti on the roofs of cars.

An old-gold fox steps gingerly into your pale
    hinterland;
his cold cunning matches your moon-chill.

Frost-filled wanderer – luckless and hardened
    to ice-silver –
your lone observer salutes you, Cold-Heart Moon.

*John Rice*

# The Harvest Moon

It is the Harvest Moon! On gilded vanes
  And roofs of villages, on woodland crests
  And their aerial neighborhoods of nests
  Deserted, on the curtained window-panes
Of rooms where children sleep, on country lanes
  And harvest-fields, its mystic splendor rests!
  Gone are the birds that were our summer
  guests,
  With the last sheaves return the laboring wains!
All things are symbols: the external shows
  Of Nature have their image in the mind,
  As flowers and fruits and falling of the leaves;
The song-birds leave us at the summer's close,
  Only the empty nests are left behind,
  And pipings of the quail among the sheaves.

*Henry Wadsworth Longfellow (1807–1882)*

# Tell Me

Tell me about
moondust floating in the moonlight
of the supermoon;
how you were moonstruck
and howling at the wolf moon,
at the blood moon bleeding in the sky,
hearing the call of the hunter's moon;
how there was nowhere to hide
from the huge orange harvest moon;
how curious you were to see the crescent moon
pass from a gibbous moon to the glorious full moon
then fade into a waning moon;
and I'll tell you about
the Dark Side
of the Moon.

*Jilly Pryor*

# The Crescent Moon

Slipping softly through the sky
　Little horned, happy moon,
Can you hear me up so high?
　Will you come down soon?

On my nursery window-sill
　Will you stay your steady flight?
And then float away with me
　Through the summer night?

Brushing over tops of trees,
　Playing hide and seek with stars,
Peeping up through shiny clouds
　At Jupiter or Mars.

I shall fill my lap with roses
　Gathered in the milky way,
All to carry home to mother.
　Oh! what will she say!

Little rocking, sailing moon,
　Do you hear me shout — Ahoy!
Just a little nearer, moon,
　To please a little boy.

*Amy Lowell (1874–1925)*

# The Man in the Moon

The Man in the Moon as he sails the sky,
Is a very remarkable skipper;
But he made a mistake when he tried to take
A drink of milk from the Dipper.
He dipped it into the Milky Way,
And slowly and carefully filled it;
The Big Bear growled, and the Little Bear howled,
And scared him so that he spilled it!

*Anon*
A traditional American children's moon tale

# The Cow in the Moon

Look, said the cow
there's a cow's face
In
the
Mooooooooo
ooon

*Roger Stevens*

# Mooncalf

The moon grew full and swollen
and knew she'd soon give birth.
She drew the clouds around her
to veil her from the earth.

But all the cows were waiting
in the pasture down below
to greet the little mooncalf and
admire its milky glow.

They stood in hopeful silence
looking to the skies
and listening for the faintest sound
of its first mooing cries.

Suddenly a moonbeam
pushed the cloud away
and there all washed in moonlight
the newborn mooncalf lay.

They heard it moo. It raised its head.
And then it tried to stand.
It shimmered on unsteady legs,
a sailor new to land.

# Transformed

When day turns to night
and the last gleam of light
from the sun fades away into dark,

when the bright full moon shines
through the cracks in the blinds
and my skin feels its silvery spark,

then I leap from my chair,
growing claws, sprouting hair,
and I bound for the door, breaking through.

My heart races faster.
The moon is my master.
I gaze up and howl, "Ahhhrooooooo!"

The cows still moo the story of
the magic of this night.
Cow-dreams were changed forever by
the mooncalf made of light.

*Kate O'Neil*

# The Moon Fell Down

The moon fell down.
It landed in the street in front of my house.
It was much smaller than anyone had expected,
though nonetheless beautiful
with its thousands of craters
and creamy color of burnished marble.

It was slightly taller than a tree
and wide enough to block traffic in both directions.
We gathered around it and wondered whom to call.
The mayor? An astronomer?
Is there a person in charge of the tides?

My mother told me not to get too close.
I believe I saw Neil Armstrong's footprints
along with leftover pieces of the lunar module,
which looked as tiny as a toy.

And later that night, when my mother wasn't
    looking,
I went out front and touched the moon.
My mother saw the dust on my fingers when
    I returned
and knew I had disobeyed.

She told the moon, 'You'll have to go home now.'
The moon then rose back into the sky
where it remains to this day.

*Robert Schechter*

The cows still moo the story of
the magic of this night.
Cow-dreams were changed forever by
the mooncalf made of light.

*Kate O'Neil*

# The Moon Fell Down

The moon fell down.
It landed in the street in front of my house.
It was much smaller than anyone had expected,
though nonetheless beautiful
with its thousands of craters
and creamy color of burnished marble.

It was slightly taller than a tree
and wide enough to block traffic in both directions.
We gathered around it and wondered whom to call.
The mayor? An astronomer?
Is there a person in charge of the tides?

My mother told me not to get too close.
I believe I saw Neil Armstrong's footprints
along with leftover pieces of the lunar module,
which looked as tiny as a toy.

And later that night, when my mother wasn't
    looking,
I went out front and touched the moon.
My mother saw the dust on my fingers when
    I returned
and knew I had disobeyed.

She told the moon, 'You'll have to go home now.'
The moon then rose back into the sky
where it remains to this day.

*Robert Schechter*

# Transformed

When day turns to night
and the last gleam of light
from the sun fades away into dark,

when the bright full moon shines
through the cracks in the blinds
and my skin feels its silvery spark,

then I leap from my chair,
growing claws, sprouting hair,
and I bound for the door, breaking through.

My heart races faster.
The moon is my master.
I gaze up and howl, "Ahhhroooooooo!"

*Diana Murray*

# Moon Dragons

Moon Dragons soar
Over craters and mountains,
Moon Dragons sip
At the dust from dry fountains,
Moon Dragons snack
On nebula flowers,
Moon Dragons bathe
In asteroid showers,

*Moon Dragon, Moon Dragon*
*Take me away,*
*Away to the stars*
*Where Moon Dragons play.*

Moon Dragons float
With whispers for wings,
Moon Dragons bask
On Saturn's soft rings,
Moon Dragons race
To bright satellites,
Moon Dragons feast
On hot meteorites.

*Moon Dragon, Moon Dragon*
*Take me away,*
*Away to the stars*
*Where Moon Dragons play.*

Moon Dragons drift
With thistledown grace,
Moon Dragons croon
In the glow of deep space,
Moon Dragons swim
In infinite night,
Moon Dragons sleep
On cushions of light.

*Moon Dragon, Moon Dragon*
*Take me away,*
*Away to the stars*
*Where Moon Dragons play.*

*J. H. Rice*

# The Wish

It was so near, I had to try...
I took the ladder from the loft
I rowed the boat far out to sea
And there it hung, so bright, so soft

I held the ladder up... it touched!
The boat rocked hard, but up I went
Into the white, the dust and cold
Around me, a familiar scent

I took a giant step for man
And floated in the eerie sky
The ladder fell into the sea
I heard it splash. I laughed
Goodbye

But now I wish I could return
I want things as they were before...
To see the moon from Mother Earth
To rock my little boat once more

*Andrea Shavick*

# The Cat and the Moon

The cat went here and there
And the moon spun round like a top,
And the nearest kin of the moon
The creeping cat looked up.
Black Minnaloushe stared at the moon,
For wander and wail as he would
The pure cold light in the sky
Troubled his animal blood.
Minnaloushe runs in the grass,
Lifting his delicate feet.
Do you dance, Minnaloushe, do you dance?
When two close kindred meet
What better than call a dance?
Maybe the moon may learn,
Tired of that courtly fashion,
A new dance turn.
Minnaloushe creeps through the grass
From moonlit place to place,
The sacred moon overhead
Has taken a new phase.
Does Minnaloushe know that his pupils
Will pass from change to change,
And that from round to crescent,
From crescent to round they range?

Minnaloushe creeps through the grass
Alone, important and wise,
And lifts to the changing moon
His changing eyes.

*W.B. Yeats (1865–1939)*

# A Goodnight Moon

A thin silver needle
stitches the moon to the sky
like a pearl button

reflecting
dark blue clouds
with bright edges

a patchwork
of indigo, purple
and soft grey.

It's like a quiet sea, calmed
by barely breathing breezes.
Time for my curtains to close

to whisper goodnight.
For my eyes to fall
asleep,

*David Harmer*

# About the Editor and the Illustrator

**Roger Stevens** visits schools, libraries and festivals performing his work and running workshops for young people and teachers. He is a National Poetry Day Ambassador, a founding member of the Able Writers scheme with Brian Moses, and runs the award-winning poetry website www.poetryzone.co.uk for children and teachers. He has published over forty books for children, including *The Waggiest Tails*, for Otter-Barry Books, with Brian Moses, illustrated by Ed Boxall and in 2018 won the prestigious North Somerset Teachers' Book Award for poetry. He spends his time between the Loire, in France, and Brighton, where he lives with his wife and his very shy dog, Jasper.

**Ed Boxall** is an illustrator, writer, performer and educator. He has written and illustrated many picture books such as *Francis the Scaredy Cat* and *Mr Trim and Miss Jumble*. His passion for poetry shows in his illustration work – he has illustrated for some of the UK's top children's poets such as Brian Moses, Roger Stevens and James Carter. Ed had his own full length collection of children's poems, *Me and My Alien Friend*, published in 2018. Ed performs and runs workshops with children, using an exciting mix of spoken word, projections, giant story books and music. www.edboxall.com